More

Man in Garden

AND

Man in Factory

Larry

MUSEUM PRESS

First published in book form in Great Britain by
Museum Press Limited
39 Parker Street, London WC2
1967

© 1965, 1966 Punch Publications Ltd

*The Artist and Publishers wish to express their thanks
to Punch Publications Ltd., for permission to reproduce
these drawings, all of which first appeared in Punch*

Printed in Great Britain by
Lowe & Brydone (Printers) Ltd. London

G.3305

B

"*Timber!*"

c

MAN IN FACTORY

D

EXHIBITION
IN AID OF
CHILDRENS'
XMAS
PARTY
FUND

OUT

IN